Good times
in Seattle!

David Enlow

A DAY AT THE ZOO IN 2062

An Odd Collection of Short Stories
& Doodles for Grown-ups

Written by: Daniel Eachus

Illustrations by: Diego Parada

1st Edition

(that's why there are so many mistakes)

This is a work of fiction. Names, characters, places, and incidents either are the product of the author's imagination or are used fictitiously. Any resemblance to actual persons, living or dead, events, or locales is entirely coincidental.

Publisher's Cataloging-in-Publication data

Eachus, Daniel, author. | Parada, Diego, illustrator.

A day at the zoo in 2062 : an odd collection of short stories & doodles for grown-ups / written by Daniel Eachus ; illustrations by Diego Parada

Los Angeles, CA: Daniel Eachus and Diego Parada, 2021.

LCCN: 2020925520 | ISBN: 978-1-63760-484-7

LCSH Short stories, American. | American wit and humor. | Humorous stories. | Humorous fiction. | BISAC FICTION / Short Stories (single author) | FICTION / Humorous / General

LCC PS3605.A34 D39 2021 | DDC 813.6--dc23

danieleachus.com

yesdiegoparada.com

To The Haters

"Some people need vitamins that look and taste like gummy bears."

-Me, *I said that.*

CONTENTS

FOREWORD

When Daniel asked me to do a foreword in his book, my first thought was, "Who?" I think it was his way of asking me out. I'm still not completely sure. Then, I saw that illustrations were being done by Diego Parada. I'd never heard of him either. It was all so confusing to me. I got paid, so I agreed, but I really don't know what to say. I'm as anxious as you are to see what this book is about. I've set my bar very low. I hope you have too.

-Sandra, *works at the mall*

INTRODUCTION

Half a score and one year ago, I challenged myself to write a short story. That short story became a full notebook of short stories, which later turned into two complete notebooks of short stories, and eventually, a giant waste of time.

You see, those notebooks collected dust in a filing cabinet for a decade. I did nothing with them. I showed nobody. They were just things I could tell myself I did one time when I was bored.

Then, one day, I came across those lonesome notebooks and waded through them. A funny sensation came over me, I laughed.

Now, I laugh at my own jokes all the time, but never did I expect to laugh at one of my short stories. These stories weren't as bad as I had remembered.

So, I polished my favorite ones up, wrote a couple dozen more, and suckered my good friend Diego into drawing a bunch of pictures to go along with them.

What began as a giant waste of time grew into...

A DAY AT THE ZOO IN 2062

THE SNIFFLY CASE OF
MURPHY SMOOTH

Murphy Smooth has a unique gift. He can make anyone fall in love with him, just by sneezing on them. If an attractive woman walks by, all Murphy has to do is sneeze on her, and she'll fall madly in love with him. Murphy used his gift as often as you would imagine. He hooked up with beautiful woman after beautiful woman.

Until, one day, Murphy caught a terrible cold. It was so bad that he couldn't control his sneezing. Murphy caused a whole elevator full of people to fall in love with him – men, women, and even a small dog inside of a stroller (the backs of Murphy's legs were sore for weeks). Murphy even went to his grandmother's house and accidentally sneezed on her (he always got the best Christmas gifts after that).

It was out of control. So, Murphy did what he never had to do before. He covered his mouth. It sounds so easy. It seems like a simple solution. Murphy stopped sneezing on people altogether, but there was a problem. You see, when Murphy covered his mouth, his hands fell in love with him.

Now, every time Murphy looks at an attractive woman, he slaps the shit out of himself.

CIGARETTE PARTY

I threw a cigarette party today in my apartment. People from all rooms came together for the lighting of the uneventful, miniature torches. Some came for the aroma. Others came for the lack of atmosphere. There was even a group of rock singers who came by to grunge-up their voices. Ah, cigarette parties. They would be so much more fun if I smoked.

IF YOU GIVE A MAN A BEER

If you give a man a beer, he will surely say, "Thank you." If you give a man two beers, he will be your friend. If you give a man three beers, he will be your best friend. If you give a man four beers, he will never forget you. If you give a man five beers, he will forget your name. If you give a man six beers, he will start to annoy you. If you give a man seven beers, you will start to annoy him. If you give a man eight beers, he will start to annoy himself. If you give a man nine beers, he will angrily question what you're trying to do. If you give a man ten beers, he'll forget everything, and he will surely say, "Thank you."

9

DON'T BE AFRAID
OF THE DARK

So many children (and some adults) are afraid of the dark. It keeps them awake at night. It prevents them from feeling well-rested and energized. Are you one of those children (or broken adults)? If so, allow me to calm your fear.

First off, I want you to know that being afraid of the dark is irrational. Darkness is merely the absence of light. It's half of our day. I mean, imagine having a solar eclipse. Then, the darkness would last even longer, and that's just one scenario. A comet could hit the Earth at any moment, hurdling clouds of dust into the atmosphere, and blocking out sunlight for weeks and maybe months. Think of the chaos that would bring.

And let's not forget chaos causes war. The death and destruction of wars are happening all around us. A war could break out right where you live at the snap of a finger. Someone could drop a bomb on your house. At least then, no one would want to rob it.

That's right! Anyone could rob your house at any time. Right now, burglars could be breaking into your home, ready to slit your throat and take everything you own. I mean, you'd be dead if that happened. You can't survive a slit throat. Well, you can, but you could die of a heart attack just from the stress.

Then again, heart attacks could happen at any moment as well. There's also: brain aneurysms, cancers, strokes, diabetes, influenza, pneumonia, chronic lower respiratory disease, car accidents, bike accidents, boat accidents, Alzheimer's, kidney disease, septicemia, cirrhosis, and of course, spontaneous combustion (to name a few).

Death is literally at your doorstep. And you will die. You most definitely will die!

So, yeah... don't be afraid of the dark.

LITTLE BOY BLUE

Little Boy Blue, don't blow your horn. Go to the doctor. You shouldn't be blue. Humans aren't blue. Put down your horn, and go find out what's wrong with you.

MANSPLAINING

My girlfriend and I got into an argument last night. She said I need to stop mansplaining things to her. Mansplaining! It's when a man explains something to a woman in a condescending way.

So, like, let's say you're a woman, and you work at a bank. You've worked there for over a decade. Mansplaining would be if I, as a patron (a patron is just another word for a customer), came up to you and started explaining how bank loans work. Of course, you know how bank loans work. You work at a bank!

Granted, not all bank tellers deal with handling loans. Some just work behind the counter, processing deposits or withdrawals. So, it's possible that you didn't actually know that much about how bank loans work. Regardless, it's still mansplaining.

An easy way to remember: mansplaining is just the words *man* and *explaining* pushed together. Pretty cool, huh?

Man, I need to tell this to my girlfriend.

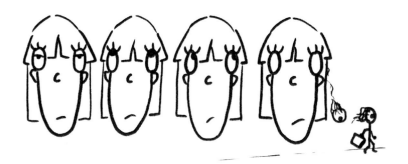

GHOST DIARIES:
DAY 1

First day out ghosting. You know, in every ghost movie and *Scooby-Doo* episode I saw when I was alive, ghosts haunted houses, mansions, hospitals, closets, and cemeteries. So, it must be a mistake that I was assigned to an empty house. Like, literally, nobody lives here. Today, I sat in a room for eleven hours turning the lights on and off. That was it. I got excited when I noticed a spider in the corner of the room. By *excited*, I mean, I screamed. Even in death, I'm scared of spiders. I hope this gets better.

GHOST DIARIES:
DAY 2

Day two. Still stuck in this empty house. Tonight, the lights kept flickering on and off. I wasn't doing that. WTF!? I wasn't doing that! Who was doing that?

THE JOKE ON JERRY'S FOREHEAD

Anybody who met Jerry would instantly laugh. Jerry would have them on their knees, with tears coming out of their nostrils, they were laughing so hard. The thing is, Jerry wasn't the least bit funny. Jerry knew that the reason people were laughing was because he had the funniest joke in the world on his forehead.

The trouble was, Jerry couldn't see it. It was invisible to him, and people would break up hysterically before they could ever tell him what the joke was. It was *that* funny! Jerry loved it though and decided that he didn't care what the joke was, as long as it made people laugh. Good thing too. Because the truth of it was… Jerry just had a funny-looking forehead.

APRIL FOOL'S EVE

Tomorrow is the notorious anti-holiday known as *April Fool's Day*. I've been fearing this day all year. I hate it so much. Every year I'm tricked. I'm outfoxed. I'm laughed at. But not this year. No, this year will be different. This year, I'm ready. I'm taking every necessary and unnecessary precaution for the sake of my mental and social safety.

First, I've locked myself in a cold, dark, empty room, where no one can find me. I even drove here with my eyes closed to make sure I didn't know where I was going. I couldn't tell you where I am right now, even if I wanted to.

Next, I took away all of my food, water, clothes, and entertainment. I'm naked and miserable at the moment, which means that no one can embarrass me tomorrow, because I have already embarrassed myself.

Finally, I rigged the space I'm in with explosives, so that if anyone somehow manages to find me, the second they open the door, the entire building will explode, killing me inside. Thus, ruining their attempt at an April Fool's Day prank.

Hahaha! It's perfect! Who's the fool now, huh?! Who is the fool now?!

THE POEM SHAKESPEARE WROTE
RIGHT AFTER HE DIED

COLLEGE
DRINKING STORIES

AT THE PARTY.

"I'm barely even buzzed."

THE NEXT MORNING.

"I was pretty drunk last night."

A WEEK LATER.

"You guys remember that party last week when I blacked out?"

99 YEARS AND
1 HORRIBLE NIGHT

For the past 99 years, Felonious Sharpe would go to bed at precisely 9:21 pm every night. He would wake up at exactly 5:59 am and start his day. However, this day was different. This day, Felonious did not wake up at exactly 5:59 am. The night before, when Felonious went to bed at precisely 9:21 pm, he got stuck in a nightmare.

It was the worst nightmare Felonious had ever dreamt of. He was trapped in an ice storm during a hurricane that formed right after an earthquake that was caused by a tornado in the middle of a great fire.

It didn't take long for Felonious to begin gasping for air. He couldn't breathe. He could barely react. He tried snapping his fingers, in hopes of making it all disappear, but the flames from the fire slowly and painfully singed off his hands. Without hands, Felonious bled profusely.

Devastated by what he was looking at, his eyes exploded. That didn't help his heart, which physically tore itself in half from the pain. He dropped to his knees so intently that his bones shattered. Fragments of cartilage ripped away into the abyss.

"Fuck!" Felonious screamed, with his collapsed lungs' last breath.

At 5:58 am that morning, Felonious died a gruesome death. Not just in his nightmare but in reality too. Felonious was gone for good.

His family stood over his lifeless body that morning, sobbing and sniffling. Together they were comforted by the same thought, "Thank God, he died in his sleep."

LIFE'S GREAT QUESTIONS

Why do we call it green tea when it's yellow and brown? Are Mosquito Eaters allowed to eat anything else? Do Siamese Cats cough up skin balls? What are we supposed to call fake spam? Who *did* let the dogs out? What's wrong with clouds one through eight? Are people in comas just following their dreams?

...these are some of life's great questions.

GHOST DIARIES:
DAY 84

A couple of people walked into the house today. These two teenagers brought a Ouija board with them. I'm not going to lie, I was thrilled to finally have people to scare.

There was a problem though. I realized I didn't know how to use a Ouija board. I mean, I know how to use it, but not as a ghost. I couldn't get it to go where I wanted it to.

When I finally figured the stupid thing out, the teenagers started asking me questions about things I didn't know the answers to. "Who keeps flickering the lights?" I don't know! I'm still trying to figure that out. It's really not me.

Before I could think of how to respond, the girl asked another question, "How old is this house?" Another question I didn't know the answer to. I quickly made up a number, "One hundred and five years old."

The boy knew it was wrong. He grabbed the Ouija board. "This place isn't haunted," he snickered. The teenagers turned off the light switch and left.

At least there's no more flickering.

JUNGLE TALK

The lion said, "Roar!" The snake said, "Hssssss." The monkey said, "Oo-oo-ah-ah!" The cougar said, "Buy me a beer, and let's go back to your place!"

IDENTITY FOR SALE

I sold my fingerprints online today. I just took them off, stuck them in an envelope, and put them in the mail. Some middle-aged guy in Florida bought them. He said he was going through an identity crisis.

Why not sell them? I didn't need them anymore. I know who I am. Plus, I have a driver's license. That has my face and name printed right on it. I can also just ask my friends if I ever forget. "Hey, who am I?" They'll know.

Just as the fingerprints were sent off, I got an email from the man who bought them. "How will I know that these fingerprints are yours?" he asked. This question baffled me. I told him that I didn't really know how to prove it.

Three weeks later, two police officers came to my door, and I was thrown in jail for robbing a bank back East. After being locked up for several days, I received a letter. It was the man who bought my fingerprints. The letter read:

"Fingerprints work great. Thanks!"

MY DOG ATE
MY HOMEWORK

My dog ate my homework. My teacher thought I was lying. So, the next day, I turned in a pile of dog shit.

BEER PONG CHAMPS

It was down to this: one cup in the back-left corner for Rob and Bobby. For Kim and Kirsten, a single cup straight down the middle. It was Kim and Kirsten's turn to throw their beer pong balls.

Kim's shot: airball.

Kirsten: a near miss.

Rob and Bobby washed off their beer pong balls in a filthy cup of dirt water. Rob tossed his ball. It ricocheted off the side of the cup. Kim scoffed from the other side of the table. She turned to her partner Kirsten, "These guys don't stand a chance."

She turned back to the table. Bobby's ball wasn't in his hand. It was hopping across the table. A bounce! Kim lunged towards the ball, but it was too late. The ball landed perfectly into the last cup. According to house rules, it was game over. Rob and Bobby had won.

The room went wild. The crowd hoisted Rob and Bobby into the air. Everyone began to chant, "Beer pong champs! Beer pong champs!" The energy was electric.

The next morning, Rob and Bobby went into work, their chests puffed up against their chins, as they walked through the office. Their boss, Megan, rounded the corner. "Rob! Bobby!" she hollered. Rob smirked, "Good morning." Megan didn't smile back. She questioned the men, "Why are you both two hours late?"

Bobby couldn't wait to tell her. He perked up as the words shot through his lips, "We were up celebrating late last night. Rob and I won beer pong!" Megan replied quickly, "You're fired."

Rob and Bobby packed up their desks and left. None of their co-workers made eye contact. Not a single person spoke a word. Rob and Bobby walked out quietly. Nobody cared that they were beer pong champs.

THE EXPERT

My name is Hippolytus, and I am an expert on *words*. Words are good. Words are important. Words would not be as important, however, without the ideas they convey. So, I guess, actually, I'm an expert on *ideas*. Ideas are really, really good, and they're also important. Although, ideas wouldn't be worth much at all without *things*. Things are wonderful (sometimes), and they're crucial to ideas. So, really, I'm an expert on things. See, but things wouldn't exist at all without *nothing*. Nothing is what makes things possible. So, in the end, I suppose, I'm an expert on nothing.

HIPPOLYTUS

47

BE THANKFUL

The world is a negative place. So, here are some positive things that you can wake up every day feeling thankful for:

LIGHT BULBS.

Be thankful for light bulbs, because life would be much more dangerous, if every time you had an idea, you got a flame over your head.

CHRISTMAS CARDS.

Be thankful for Christmas cards, because without them, you might never know that your mailbox still works.

NEIGHBORS.

Be thankful for neighbors, because if you didn't have them, whose fireworks would you watch from your front lawn every 4th of July?

TELEVISION.

Be thankful for television, because sometimes you need to take a break from being on your phone all day, so that you can be antisocial while looking at a bigger screen.

FAMILY.

Be thankful for family, because without them, you wouldn't have a Netflix password.

Remember to be thankful for things in life, because if you're not thankful, then you're an ungrateful piece of shit.

INTERMISSION

You have now reached the halfway point of the book. It's time for a brief intermission. This is your chance to pee-pee or poo-poo as much as you need to.

Not enough books give you this opportunity. You have to set the book down on a filthy table or worse, take it with you while you take a dump. Sure, it's great to have a book with you as you unload into the crapper, but what about when you finish? You need both hands to wipe.

Yeah, the physical act of cleaning your butthole only takes one hand, but everybody knows that tearing off the toilet paper is a two-hand job. One hand is placed on the roll, itself. The other hand does the tearing motion. Unless, that is, you only use one-ply TP, and in that case, you're a monster who shouldn't even be reading this book right now!

Anyways, I've made you hold onto your turtlehead long enough. Go. Relieve yourself, and resume reading whenever you're ready.

...and now, back to the book.

THE MOST BEAUTIFUL
WOMAN IN THE WORLD

Today I saw the most beautiful woman in the world. She was so dazzling, that I threw-up when we made eye contact. She was so incredibly gorgeous, that I don't think I'll eat for a month. I mean, this woman was so absolutely, wonderfully breathtaking, that I changed my relationship status online to *It's Complicated*, so everyone knows that, emotionally, I'm taken.

I just had to show this woman to my best friend Ryan. So, I did. Ryan looked at her, turned to me, and said, "She's a six."

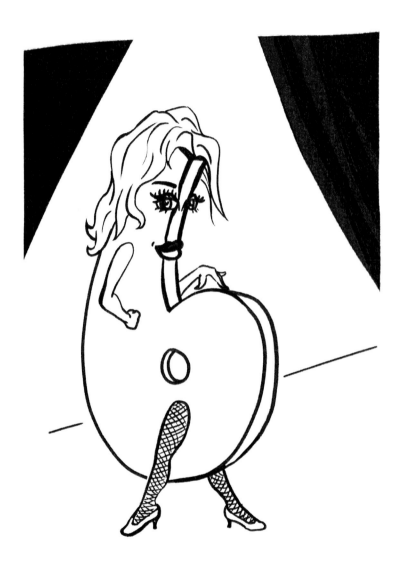

LESSONS TO LIVE
AND DIE BY

1. Never buy a used treadmill from someone who's overweight. Clearly, it doesn't work.

2. Don't live every day like it's your last. You'll get tired of crying.

3. Never poke a sleeping bear... unless it's sleeping on top of you.

4. When life gives you lemons, next time ask for money.

5. Always be yourself... unless you're an asshole.

SPLIT PERSONALITY

The doctor confirmed it. I have what is known as a split personality. One side of me is really, really cool and the other side is awesome.

It's pretty tough for me to deal with. Half of my friends are really, really cool and the other half are awesome.

People are always so confused when they see me hanging around such vastly different crowds. It's even hard for me to get a girlfriend, because sometimes, when I'm on a date, I'll act totally awesome, and then out of nowhere, I'll be ridiculously cool.

I hope these words even make sense to you, because I keep switching back and forth.

Life is incredibly difficult when your body can't choose whether it wants to be awesome or really, really cool. So, instead of choosing, I've decided... I'll just be average.

REX THE TALKING DOG

My dog Rex is no ordinary dog. In fact, Rex is the most extraordinary animal on Earth, because he is the only dog in the world who can talk.

It's true! He can actually talk. No other animal can speak like we do, except Rex. It's truly amazing! I'll ask Rex what kind of food he wants, and he'll answer right back. It's an absolute miracle!

The only downside is that Rex is also deaf, so when he talks, it sounds just like he's barking.

Nobody's perfect.

BREATHTAKING

When Stuart met Samantha, she took his breath away. He suffocated and died.

KISSED BY A PRINCESS

Once upon a time, there was a beautiful princess. She needed to find herself a prince, or else an undesirable marriage would be arranged for her. That was the last thing the princess wanted. So, she swiped and swiped on dating apps but never could find the perfect prince.

One night, she was crying on her balcony, when suddenly, a frog jumped up onto the railing. She wiped away her tears and began talking to the frog. She told him of her dating woes and how she needed to find the perfect prince. The frog sat there. He was such a good listener.

The princess rambled on and on. She got so excited, she bent down and kissed the frog. Suddenly, as if by some sort of miracle, that kiss turned... into warts... which became an infection... which led to public embarrassment... which forced her to run away from the kingdom... lose her crown... and wander the streets without a home, like a beggar.

The moral of the story is: Don't kiss a frog when you don't know where the hell he's been.

WHEN THE WORLD WILL END

Alas! I did it! I successfully invented a time machine for the sole purpose of going into the future and finding out when the world will end. I sent my assistant, Corky, to find out the exact date, but Corky never came back.

I guess he found it.

THAT MOVIE TRAILER WAS GOOD, BUT THE WRITTEN VERSION WAS SO MUCH BETTER

"How bad was it?" asks an older man, struck with fear, expressed dominantly by his quivering lower lip.

Another younger man in a dark room with a faint candle illuminating the right side of his face swallows hard and mutters, "Bad..."

(BOOM sound)

A young, attractive girl bleeding from above her left eyebrow looks around, breathing heavily.

There is a man with an evil grin.

"Stop it! Stop it! You will not murder the only man I've ever loved!" screams a middle-aged housewife.

(bigger BOOM sound)

"Kill him," says a mysterious voice that is believed to be the younger man.

The older man looks like Leonardo DiCaprio.

COMING.

A car blows up.

THIS.

The older man hangs off of the edge of a building.

SUMMER.

The middle-aged housewife smiles. The young girl cries and hugs a dog.

Suddenly, everything goes dark. Silence. The movie title is revealed.

"I'll be waiting Daddy," whispers a creepy little girl.

(final BOOM sound)

JUNE 21st appears and then fades out.

Ceci n'est pas une pop-corn.

WATER BORES ME

Water is boring. It's so plain. I would much rather have brightly colored water or fruit-flavored water. Ooh, sugary water! That would be the best. Hot chocolate water... mmm, I can taste it now. Or maybe some carbonated bubbly water. Water with tea! Water with coffee! Wait... what's this? Water in a bottle? Hm. I'd pay $4 to see what that tastes like.

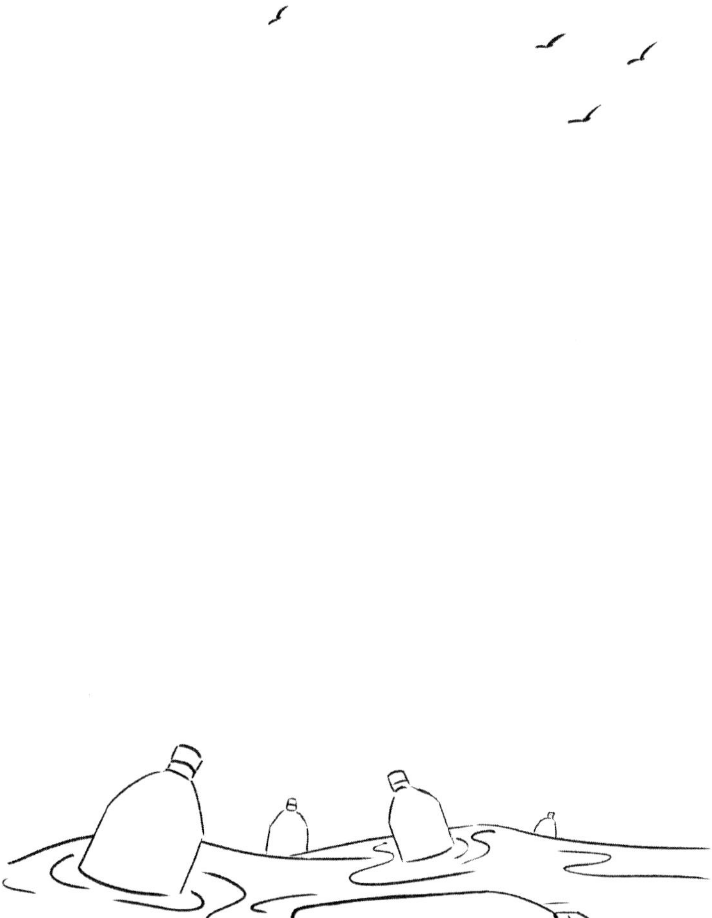

STRANDED ON
AN ISLAND

For the past two months, I've been stranded on an island. At least, I think it's an island. I'm assuming it is, because no one ever gets stranded on a peninsula.

All I have is this pen and paper. I'm still trying to figure out how to make a raft out of it.

My goal is to have a concrete plan by Tuesday. The problem is I haven't known what day of the week it is for two months now. I know I've been here for sixty-seven days, but I can't, for the life of me, remember if I arrived here on a Monday or a Thursday. I just know it wasn't a Saturday. That, I know for sure.

I guess, while I'm writing this, I should use the opportunity to officially apologize to all of the birds here on the island. I've been walking around naked every day. I'm sorry to all of the animals who have had to see me like this, and I especially want to apologize to the two birds I injured after they tried nesting in my privates. I had to hurt them. They were woodpeckers.

I also want to put it out there that I made love to a coconut on Day 12. Anyways, carry on, civilized world. I'll see you soon.

SPIDER ON THE WALL

Spider! It sat there staring at me menacingly from the wall. I tried squashing it with a tissue, but it escaped my grasp. I couldn't let it get away, so I did what I had to do. I shot it with a gun. I wounded one of its feet, but the spider kept on crawling. I did the next best thing. I pulled out a knife and tried stabbing it, but the spider was too quick. So, I blew up my house.

No more spider.

DATE SMART!

Everyone told me to try the online dating thing. I had resisted for years. There are too many crazies on those apps. I'd heard the stories - all of those unsuspecting people getting catfished. I sure as heck didn't want to get catfished!

I had my reservations, but I was also tired of being single. "Fine," I finally said, "I'll give it a whirl."

Two months in now, and I'm really starting to get the hang of it. There's an art behind it, you see.

So, like, a few weeks ago, I was swiping through the app, and I found the perfect woman. I don't use the word *perfect* lightly, but she was it; a ten from head to toe. So, of course, I passed on her. I said, "No, thanks." A woman that beautiful has to be a catfish, and I wasn't about to be fooled so easily.

A week later, I finally matched with someone else. I deleted her. She had to be fake.

A couple of days after that, I got another match. This time, she wrote to me, "Hey, how are you?" Ha! Seriously? Like she actually cares about how I'm doing. Nobody does that these days, sister! I quickly unmatched her. Blocked. I had her banned from the app.

Then, just yesterday, I went on my very first actual date with a woman I met online. I'll be honest, I was nervous. We went out to dinner at a fancy restaurant. Her conversation was wonderful. Her beauty was unmatched. I had her arrested. I wasn't about to be tricked.

It's been a long two months. I'm still single. Still looking. But I'm happy to say: I've never been catfished.

BEWARE OF
THE PLAYOFFS

Beware of something in sports called: The Playoffs. If you become exposed to someone watching his or her favorite sports team during this time of year, there are some rules you must adhere to, for your safety and for... ok, yeah, mostly for your safety.

<u>RULE #1</u>: **If the television stops working, stand in the center of the room.** The person watching the playoffs will first start hitting the TV. It *will* become violent. After the television inevitably doesn't turn back on (because hitting it never helps), the playoff watcher will begin looking for a radio (wherever the hell that might be). It will be hard to find. It will be buried. Standing

in the center of the room is the safest place to be during this time.

RULE #2: **While watching the game, always stand in the back of the room.** Throwing things at the television is normal for a playoff watcher. You never want to be in the line of fire. A flying remote can kill a person. There will be projectiles.

RULE #3: **If the playoff watcher's team loses, move away.** I don't mean, move across the room. I mean, move to another city. You don't want to be anywhere near the playoff watcher for at least a year... until the next playoffs start.

RULE #4: **If the playoff watcher's team wins, ask him/her immediately for money.** A victory excites the playoff watcher so much, you can get away with just about anything for one to two hours. This is the time to ask for cash.

However much that person has in his or her wallet, ask for it all. The playoff watcher *will* give it to you. Do not be afraid to get as much out of them as possible. They won't remember anything the next day, other than that their team won. Take advantage.

There you have it. Four simple rules to help you survive The Playoffs. It won't be easy. It will be traumatizing. Be smart. Be safe. And Godspeed during the Superbowl.

PERFECT ENGLISH

There once was a man who spoke perfect English. No one in Alabama could understand him.

GHOST DIARIES: DAY 337

I got transferred to another location! I love it. I'm in a retirement home. There's no pressure to scare anyone here. It's great. I open a cabinet and people just blame it on the wind. The other day, I turned on the TV, and some guy just sat down and started watching it. I watched it with him. I've gotten really into soap operas. Death is great!

I GAVE IT ALL AWAY

I used to have millions of dollars, you know. I used to have a big house, a fancy car, a coffee machine that brewed Italian drinks, or maybe French (I don't know. I never used it). I used to have deluxe watches and top-notch Scotches and routine face-lifts without any botches. I used to have it all. Then I gave it up.

I used to have a huge backyard. I used to have a huge front yard. I even had a decent-sized middle yard inside of my huge backyard, but I gave that up too.

I used to have a wife. I gave her up. I used to have kids. Gone. Out the door. I used to have parents, siblings, friends, neighbors, but not anymore.

I used to have a dog. I kept him (for moral support). But not the cat; not the goldfish; nor that daddy long leg who built the perfect trap in the corner of the shower but never did catch anything.

I gave everything away, so that I could have a good tax return.

I still owed.

MOST HEALTHY

Lenny has always struggled to stay healthy. So, recently, he decided it was time to make a change. Today was his first day, and he did wonderfully. For dinner, he had a salad. Just a salad! Can you believe it? Lenny was so proud of himself for being healthy, that he celebrated with ice cream, brownies, and cake.

SHOOK

The ground shook. Shelves rattled. A lone book toppled over onto its side. There was a cup of water on the nightstand. Not anymore. Reduced to a puddle. This was, most certainly, an earthquake.

The neighbors' screams infiltrated the walls. More shrieks. A chorus of panic. The shouting started, "Get under the table!" More hollering, "Move!" The bawling began. The shaking hadn't stopped. "Oh, the horror," a woman cried, "the horror!" There was nowhere to hide. Nowhere to escape.

Then... silence. Stillness.

A couple peeked out from underneath a table. The woman pulled out her phone and went straight to the internet. She looked up the size of the earthquake. What was the magnitude? The results were in: 2.1.

TREASURE
AT THE
YARD SALE

I went to a yard sale earlier. One that I won't soon forget. The lady running things said that she was just about to pack up and apologized that there wasn't very much left for me to sift through. I wasn't worried. You see, I wasn't interested in the number of items left. I was interested in just one thing... the treasure right behind her.

I couldn't imagine why this beautiful work of art was just sitting there at some stranger's yard sale. How could anyone think this was just another piece of junk? Why would anybody want to throw that away?

I hastily asked the lady in charge, "How much?" She frowned. I offered more money. The lady became angry. I upped my price. She slammed her foot down. "No," she scorned, "my grandmother is not for sale!"

I tried bargaining with the lady, but my attempts at convincing her failed time and time again. It seemed that there was no money in the world that could get this lady to sell her grandmother.

Eventually, the lady screamed, "If you don't leave right now, I'm going to call the cops!" That was that. There was no convincing her to sell.

So, when she wasn't looking, I grabbed the grandmother and took off with her.

I know I shouldn't have done that, but what was I supposed to do? I had offered up every bit of money I had to no avail.

When I got home, I unbuckled the grandmother and took her into her new home. I was finally able to speak with her for the first time. We only exchanged a few short words, when it soon became clear... I had been deceived. What I thought was hundreds of years old was only 78.

MORE OF
LIFE'S GREAT QUESTIONS

Can a hearse use the carpool lane? At what point can we start calling New York: York? If there's no "i" in *team*, why isn't there one in *solo*? Why are Pale Ales so dark? How come I've never seen a Golden Retriever come back with any gold? Do you think whoever named the ax was mad the name *chopsticks* was already taken? Why do people say they're not in shape when they're more of a shape than they were before?

...these are more of life's great questions.

A DAY
AT THE ZOO
IN 2062

I went to the zoo today for the first time. I was surprised by how small some of the cages were. Some of the photographs of the animals barely fit inside. I guess this zoo was low on money, because they had a picture of a zebra and a picture of a lion in the same cage. The hippo pictures were really old too. I was looking forward to seeing the bear pictures, but they weren't out at this time of the year. The same thing happened with the snake photos in the reptile house, because those cages had to be cleaned. Overall, it just felt good to get out and appreciate the wonders of nature.

ALTERNATE TITLES

Writing a book is hard. Writing a title for a book is even harder. Here are some of the alternate titles for this book that didn't make the cut:

And You Thought You Didn't Like To Read Before!

.

Helping Me Pay Off My Student Loans

.

It's Something To Do

.

I Thought You Said I Would Never Amount To Anything, Ms. Waterbury!?

.

Not About Turtles: A Book Not At All About Turtles

.

And then about thirty more titles that I'm not allowed to legally put in writing.

Just be glad the title is what it is.

AUTHOR'S CRITIQUES

Now that the book is complete, I've had a chance to actually look at what I wrote. There are a lot of mistakes. I'd rather not fix them. That takes work. However, I would like to point out a few of these mistakes for you now:

1.) I don't actually know what zoos will look like in 2062. If I had a time machine, I wouldn't spend my time at the zoo. Also, people won't even be able to read this book in 2062 to tell me if I'm right or wrong, because I made the books in paperback. Paperback books don't last that long. Sorry. Hardcover books are expensive.

2.) *If You Give A Man A Beer* was written entirely without ever mentioning what happens if you give a woman a beer. I can tell you that, in my personal experience, if you give a woman a beer, she will say, "Thanks, but I have a boyfriend."

3.) There are four parts to *Ghost Diaries*, and yet, ghosts don't have arms or hands. So, they can't write in a diary. Whatever.

4.) I need to point out that *Cigarette Party* also applies to vape pens. I'm sure there's a legal reason why I should point that out.

5.) Finally, hiring Diego Parada to do the illustrations was a mistake. He's very talented and good at what he does, but the energy that was created when the two of us were in a room together was very dangerous. Not good. There was a lot of toxic masculinity. By that I mean: he is toxic, and I have too much masculinity. I'm sure he would say lots of bad things about me, but I'm the one writing the words. So, it looks like I've won this round, Diego. It looks like I've won this round.

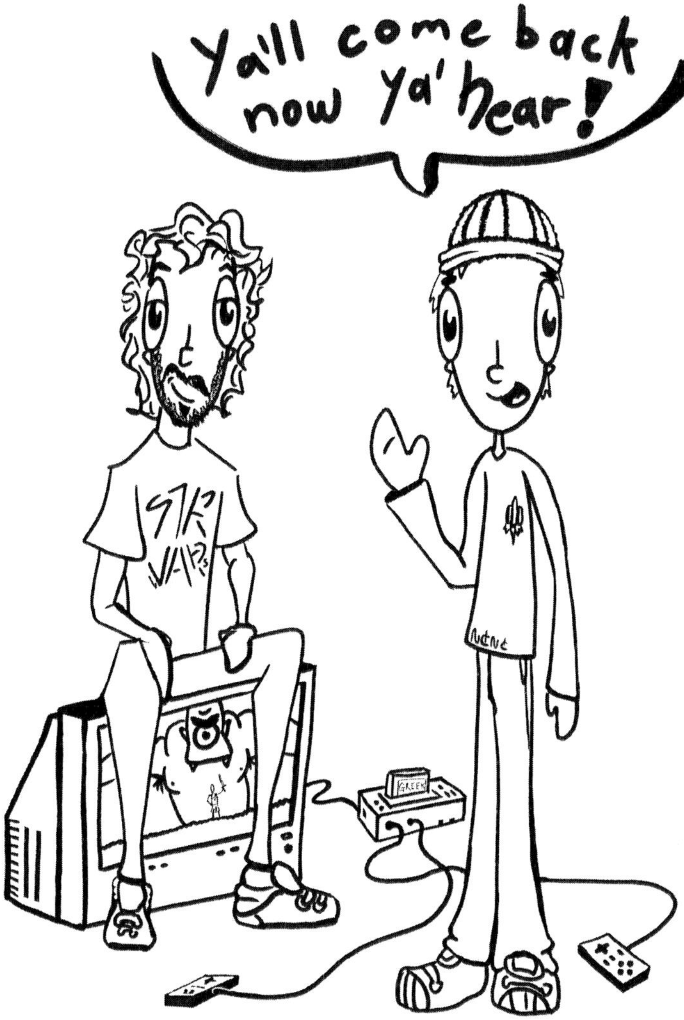
Ya'll come back now Ya' hear!
GREEK

ABOUT THE AUTHOR

DANIEL EACHUS is a writer, actor, and stand-up comedian. He has starred in over a dozen national commercials, written for the LOL Network, and made his stand-up debut on FOX and HULU's *Laughs*. He lives in Long Beach, CA, and his parents currently love him.

ABOUT THE ILLUSTRATOR

DIEGO PARADA is an actor, writer, and illustrator. He has appeared on *Modern Family*, done voiceover work on Netflix, and has starred in several national commercials. He lives in Los Angeles, CA, and his parents love him even more than they love Daniel.